D1260751

A BOY AND A BATTERY

Other Books by Raymond F. Yates

Atomic Experiments for Boys
A Boy and a Motor
The Boys' Book of Communications
The Boys' Book of Magnetism
The Boys' Book of Model Railroading
The Boys' Book of Rockets
The Boys' Book of Tools
Faster and Faster
How To Improve Your Model Railroad
Model Jets and Rockets for Boys
The Young Inventors' Guide

And, with Brock W. Yates,

Sport and Racing Cars

A BOY AND A
BATTERY

REVISED EDITION

By
RAYMOND F. YATES

*Illustrated with Photographs and
Drawings by the Author*

HARPER & BROTHERS, PUBLISHERS, NEW YORK

CONTENTS

v

ILLUSTRATIONS

vii

Chapter 1

THE ELECTRICITY MAKERS

THE great giant, Electricity, slumbered for count-
less millions of years before he was discovered and
aroused by man. The early experimenters were mys-
tified and confused. Here was a curious power that
could not be seen, weighed or heard and yet it appeared everywhere and it was eventually proven to
be a part of all things. The human race had lived
for centuries in a great sea of electricity without
knowing it. Indeed electricity is constantly flowing
through our bodies although we are unaware of its
presence. We cannot wink an eye or slightly flex a
muscle without setting up electric currents. Every
time the human or animal heart beats, it generates a

sizable amount of electric current. Electricity pervades the whole universe; it is everywhere.

There are two kinds of electricity: electricity that stands still (static) and electricity that moves (current). An ancient Greek philosopher, Thales of Miletus, who lived between the years 640 and 546 B.C., is said to have been the first to observe the strange behavior of amber after it was briskly rubbed with silk. Whether or not other early savants had noticed this curious thing is not known, but it is known that the observant Thales was the first to record the mystifying things that he saw. When amber was rubbed, it became electrically excited (charged) and it was able thereafter to pick up and hold to its surface small bits of dried leaves and pith. Thales often amused his friends with such demonstrations and they always left his home filled with awe and wonderment. What was this curious agent that defied gravity, this invisible adhesive?

But little was done about the mysterious attraction discovered by the inquisitive Thales until another able experimenter, Sir William Gilbert of England, took up where Thales had left off and found that amber shared its peculiar properties with many common articles such as resin, sulphur, glass, etc. Sir William was also quite an authority on the then ancient art of magnetism and for hours on end he fascinated his queen, Elizabeth, with his absorbing demonstrations. Indeed, it was Sir William who christened the invisible force, calling it electricity. Few are those among us who know that this word has its root in the Greek word electron, meaning amber.

The next milestone reached in the long and tortuous path of progress and discovery in electrical science bears the name of Otto von Guericke, mayor of the German city of Magdeburg. Some sixty years after Dr. Gilbert had amused and amazed the attendants of Elizabeth's court, von Guericke devised a machine for the generation of "standstill" or static electricity. No longer was he satisfied with the tedious and irksome method of rubbing amber and the other excitable materials with fur or silk. This imaginative worker mounted a ball of sulphur about the size of a basketball so that it could be revolved by turning a handle. The exciting medium was pressed against its surface and in this manner heavy charges of static electricity (the only kind known up to this time) accumulated on the surface of the sulphur. The longer and faster the sphere was turned, the greater the electric charge generated.

Machine-generated static electricity was not von Guericke's only contribution to the then black and almost satanic art of electricity. During the course of his investigations, he found that, in the case of all electrified objects, two forms of electricity appeared to be present. When an electrified rod of glass or wax was brought near a tiny ball of pith suspended from a tiny silk thread, the ball would be attracted. On the other hand, if a rod of resin was excited in the same manner, the pith ball would be repelled. This strange action brought forth many explanations. Our own Benjamin Franklin came nearest to the now known truth. He believed that electricity was a mysterious fluid, utterly invisible, weightless and formless. He reasoned further that there were two kinds of electrical fluid, one that made pith balls fall back from charged bodies and one that pulled them toward charged bodies. That was a pretty clever piece of thinking. While electricity is not a fluid (much less is it divided into two kinds), it is known that we have positive (plus) and negative (minus) electricity.

One of the greatest mysteries of electricity still remains unsolved. In which direction does electricity flow, from positive to negative or from negative to positive? The answer to that question has never been definitely established. For many years it was believed that electricity moved from negative to positive, and there were many theories put forth to support that view. Now many experts are of the opinion that the reverse is true, and a number of arguments have been advanced to support this theory also.

There is no need for the young reader of this book to concern himself with this controversy, but in reading the pages that follow, he should bear in mind that neither theory as to the direction of the flow of electricity has ever been proved.

Any boy seeking the road to knowledge in electricity would be doing himself a grave injustice if he failed to set up certain simple experimental apparatus to see for himself the electrical genii at work.

All that is really needed is a bit of pith or dried potato, a small piece of real silk thread and a rod of glass, sealing wax and some silk cloth and fur. One must be sure that all of the articles, especially the pith or the potato, are absolutely dry. A ball of either one about one-quarter inch in diameter is used and this is attached to the end of the silk thread with a very small drop of cement such as is used for the construction of model airplanes. The ball is then suspended from any object in such a way that it will be permitted to swing freely.

All objects entering into the experiment must be thoroughly dry. Otherwise results are apt to be disappointing. However, with these simple precautions and these simple materials, many interesting hours can be whiled away. The rods of glass and wax may be electrified by rubbing them briskly with the silk or the fur. When the charged rods are brought near the pith ball, it will either be pushed away by the invisible electrical forces or it will be attracted. We must not, however, confuse this attraction with magnetism.

If these experiments are continued for a sufficiently long time, one thing will become clear. It will be found that bodies bearing the same charge, as negative to negative or positive to positive, repel each other. Bodies carrying dissimilar charges, as positive to negative, attract each other. Therein lies one of the great electrical laws and if the young student of electricity does not pause long enough now to memorize it, his future experiments in the field will be difficult indeed. The matter is summed up by saying that like charges repel each other and unlike charges attract each other.

As students of electricity we must also learn to distinguish between conductors and nonconductors of electricity; that is, things or materials that will permit electricity to pass and things or materials that will not permit electricity to pass. If a list of all the materials in the world were made, it would be found that many conducted electricity very well, some very poorly and some not at all. Curiously enough, although we have only recently shown that it can bear a charge of electricity, glass must be put down as a notoriously bad conductor. Indeed, it is so bad that it is classified as an insulator. Insulators are materials used to keep electricity confined to one path or one place. They are seen on our telegraph and electric power line poles. These are the fenced-in highways over which electricity speeds.

There is a long list of electrical conductors and Stephen Grey began to discover these conductors back in the year 1729. Using a piece of wire 886 feet long, Grey stands as the first man to set up an electrical transmission line, and while only tiny amounts of force sped over the first electrical "highway," the experiment was of vast importance.

In general, it may be said that all of the metals are relatively good conductors of electricity, with silver, copper, brass and aluminum occupying the position of favorites. Even the metals, as with all class of materials, conduct in various degrees.

The next standout on the roster of famous pioneers in electricity is the French master, Charles de Cisternay du Fay. He, too, experimented with wax, resin, glass, wool, silk, pith and many other materials. He, too, like many others, set his good mind to work in pondering the many whys and wherefores of what he saw with his own eyes. Those experimenters who had passed on before him had many strange theories. One said that the mysterious attraction shown by electrified bodies was brought about by "streams which rush out of such bodies and expel the neighboring air causing small whirlwinds." Sir Kenelm Digby, an Englishman who had given some thought to the matter, ventured to hold that "chafed amber is made to emit certain rays or streams." That was in

1644. In 1632, Pierre Gassendi had said, "These electrical rays get into the pores of a straw (one of the things with which he experimented) and by means of their decussation take the better hold of it and then shrink back to the amber by which they are emitted."

Charles du Fay made a much more accurate guess. He was inclined to think that there were two kinds of electricity and he called them vitreous and resinous. The vitreous electricity he found associated with such things as glass, rock crystals, precious stones, etc. Resinous electricity he thought was associated with materials such as amber copal, gum-lac, paper, etc. Du Fay came close to the truth when he said in one of his humorous contributions to the then infant art, that "the two electricities repel themselves but attract each other."

The next great figure that appears in the story of electricity is that of our own Benjamin Franklin. His great mind also came very close to the core of the matter when he said that the strange fluid existed in two states, positive and negative. He probably thought that the negative state was merely a minus state, but he established terms and trends of thought that have stood to this very day. With his key, he also reached into the sky to pull electricity from the clouds and to prove that it was the same stuff that moved pith balls around and electrified rods of glass. Franklin went to the sky and found new and golden nuggets of knowledge.

We may now sum up, and catalogue the things we know. There is actually only one kind of electricity that exists *on* and *in* bodies in various degrees. The two states of electricity are referred to as positive and negative. When electricity is not flowing or moving, it is called static electricity. When it is moving or flowing, it is called current electricity, and this is the electricity of the everyday, workaday world.

Chapter 2

THE EARLY BATTERY MAKERS

AFTER Franklin came the battery makers and, curiously enough, they were inspired by the work that began with the twitching of a frog's leg! Luigi Galvani, an Italian physician, was conducting a biological experiment during which he dissected a frog. His helpful wife noticed that the frog's leg moved somewhat violently when she contacted certain muscles with her scalpel. What was more, the leg lay close to a charged static generator with which Galvani was also conducting experiments.

His insatiable curiosity aroused, Galvani began a long series of experiments that appeared rather trivial at the time but which turned out to be of great importance in electrical science. During these experiments, some of Galvani's less thoughtful friends called him the "Frog's Dancing Master" but their levity did not discourage him. Fortunately for mankind, he persisted in his work and finally discovered that he could make the frog's muscles twitch without the use of an electrostatic generator. Merely bringing the muscles into contact with two dissimilar metals was sufficient to bring about strong muscular action in otherwise dead tissue. Here, although he did not know it at the time, Galvani had struck upon something new. He had really discovered the electric cell, because his electricity was not generated by friction, as in rubbing glass or wax with silk or wool. A new principle was involved and although poor Galvani worked hard and long, he was never able to place his finger on it.

When, for example, he brought a piece of copper and a piece of iron together and then proceeded to contact a nerve and a muscle in the frog's leg, motion would occur. Galvani had thought that the frog's leg was the source of electricity; that somehow the contact of the metals permitted this electric current to flow. For five long years he labored and finally, in 1791, he published his now famous work on animal electricity. Buried deep in it, but still undiscovered by him, was the great principle of what is known, in honor of this great and good man, as galvanic current. A galvanic current merely means current generated by chemical action of some sort in a cell or battery.

It was the good fortune of still another Italian to find what Galvani, although he richly deserved it, had missed. Alessandro Volta took issue with the good Galvani. He thought that the seat of the electricity lay not in the frog's tissues but in the dissimilar metals and that the electric circuit or circular path was completed when these metals were touched. He was perfectly right. Galvani, without realizing it, had set up the first complete electric circuit with a chemical generator or cell.

Volta was not only an able worker and a clever theorist but he also had considerable equipment at his disposal in the University of Padua, where he had a chair. Galvani had not inspired him to continue work on frogs' legs. Volta was sure that new sources of electricity could be produced by the use of metals.

What inspired Volta to make the following classical experiment is not known. However, he separated two small discs, one of copper and the other zinc, with a piece of paper soaked in brine or solution of table salt. Still using the frog's leg but only as a detector or indicator, Volta found that rather powerful results were produced. He then added many discs of copper and zinc to his arrangement and he found that the more he added, the more powerful the effects. Indeed, he finally built a battery so powerful that it could deliver uncomfortable electric shocks to humans. Naturally, this convinced Volta that the frog's legs had nothing to do with the generation of electricity.

We can very easily duplicate Volta's first galvanic cell with a penny and a five-cent piece. Indeed, any two metals will do nicely. A piece of blotting paper is soaked in salt water and placed between the penny and the five-cent piece. The tips of a pair of old radio-phones placed on the penny and on the five-cent piece will produce a loud click, proving that electric current has been generated.

Volta cut out many small discs of copper and zinc and placed them together until he had a pile a foot high. He discovered that the higher the pile grew, the greater the shock received from his battery, for that was what it really was, although it is still called the Voltic Pile. Starting at the end of the slender thread woven by Galvani, Volta had reached the electric cell. (More than one cell is called a battery.)

Finally Volta came to his crowning achievement, his *Couronne des Tasses* or "Crown of Cups" as it was called. Into a number of earthenware cups he placed pieces of zinc and copper and a dilute solution of acid. When the zinc of the first cup was connected to the copper of the last cup, powerful electric currents flowed, the circuit or pathway having been completed. Not only was Volta able to shock his curious friends but he was also able to draw powerful sparks from his tiny powerhouse. It was all very exciting and wonderful and Volta soon became an international figure in science. The electrical unit of measurement, the volt, was named in honor of the inventor of the Pile and the Crown of Cups.

Volta was the first of a long series of battery makers. In later years there were Grove, Bunsen, Leclanché, De La Rue and many others. Many different kinds of metals and solutions were employed but each battery maker found that Volta had done a remarkably thorough piece of work and that it was rather difficult to improve upon it. He was the early lawmaker and his edicts stood fast.

In a sense, a chemical cell such as that devised by Volta is a sort of furnace in which a metal is actually consumed in the generation of electric current, just as heat is generated when coal or wood is burned. Here what the physicist calls the "law of the conservation of energy" also operates. Stated in simple terms this law holds that we cannot obtain something for nothing. For one thing, we can never really create any kind of energy. Energy can only be changed in form. When electric current is produced in a chemical cell, or battery, metal must be consumed. We can easily prove this by placing a piece of zinc and a piece of copper in a dilute solution of sulphuric acid and connecting them together. When the two elements of such a simple cell are connected in such a manner, the cell is said to be short-circuited and it will go on generating current at maximum capacity. Should this experiment be conducted, it will be seen that immediately the zinc and copper pieces (called poles or electrodes) are connected with a piece of wire, a violent gassing starts on the surface of the zinc. This will continue as long as the poles of the cell remain connected. Immediately the connection is interrupted, the gassing stops. It is only when the cell "works" that it gasses.

Should such a simple cell be set away overnight in this short-circuited condition, we should be much surprised in the morning in taking note of the damage done to the zinc. If it happened to be a thin piece of sheet zinc, we might find it entirely consumed; it would have "burned" up in our "electric furnace."

Chapter 3

MORE ABOUT BATTERIES

VOLTA made many important observations during his long investigation of electric cells and batteries. Some of his theories hardened into laws as the years passed. It was he who saw that one could roughly determine the amount of electricity generated or delivered by the amount of zinc that was consumed. The hotter the "chemical fire" the more current generated and the more metal "burned." On the other hand, the copper pole or element of the cell remained practically unchanged and Volta looked upon this as a mere connector making electrical contact with his generator.

Every electric cell has its positive and negative poles, and here let it be said that different types of cells contain different metals and that carbon often takes the place of copper because it is less expensive and, on the whole, better. The common dry cell sold in our hardware and electrical shops has a carbon pole and a zinc container which also serves as a pole and is actually consumed as the cell supplies electric current. Such cells are not, by the way, really "dry." The chemical solution used is contained in a highly absorbent mixture with which the cell is filled.

Before we can proceed much further in learning about the electric cell or battery, it will be necessary to understand the meaning of the terms "volt" and "ampere." The volt is more than the slightly abbreviated name of the great master and the ampere means far more than honor to the name of André Marie Ampère. If an electrician were questioned on the subject, he would tell us that the volt was the unit of electrical pressure and that the ampere was the unit of measurement used in estimating the volume or body of electricity.

In a sense, water power may be measured in the same manner, with the pounds per square inch in the delivery pipe as the voltage and the number of gallons delivered a minute as the amperes. Here it will be seen that a small pipe even with very high pressure (voltage) will not deliver much power because there is not a great volume to the water. A small battery providing thousands of volts may be made but it will not have a great deal of power. Indeed it may not have enough power to operate a toy motor. No young electrician should start off making the mistake of thinking that voltage alone is a measure of electric power. We could have a million volts and there would still not be enough volume of current (amperage) to ring a doorbell. The voltage is simply that part of an electric current that pushes it along through wires and conductors. It is the amperes that roll their sleeves up, as it were, and go to work.

Another mistake apt to be made by amateur electricians is that the voltage of a cell or battery will depend upon the size of the cell or battery. This is not true. We could have a dry cell the size of a barrel and one the size of a thimble and they would both deliver the same number of volts: about one and one-half. The voltage of single cells varies only within small limits. The small differences, ranging from less than a volt to nearly two volts, depend entirely upon the nature of the metals and the solution used.

Is there no difference, then, between an electric cell the size of a barrel and one the size of a thimble? There most certainly is. The larger an electric cell or battery is, the more current (amperage) it will provide. Thus, it will be clear that the amount of real power delivered by a cell or battery will, like a steam engine or an electric motor, depend upon its size.

A previous paragraph stated that Volta once built a battery with a voltage so high that he was able to shock his curious friends. Here he used many small cells connected together in the form of a large battery. It was in this manner and by adding the voltage of one cell to that of another that he was able to reach such high values. The current (amperes) and voltage of batteries can be controlled by the manner in which they are connected.

At A in the accompanying drawing (Fig. 1), we see cells connected in a series to form a battery. Should these cells have a voltage of 1½ each, the total voltage delivered would be $1\frac{1}{2} + 1\frac{1}{2} + 1\frac{1}{2} = 4\frac{1}{2}$ volts. Such simple addition would be necessary and accurate regardless of the number of cells forming the battery. On the other hand, the number of am-

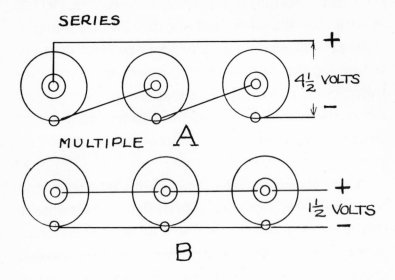

Fig. 1. How electric cells are connected to increase either voltage (as in A) or amperage or current (as in B).

peres supplied by such a battery will remain that of a single cell.

At *B* another method of computing voltage must be used. Here the cells forming the battery are connected in multiple and the voltage of the entire battery will be only the voltage of a single cell. Not so with the number of amperes delivered. If a single cell can supply a maximum of 20 amperes, then the sum total of current that can be delivered by this battery will be $20 + 20 + 20 = 60$ amperes.

By the use of simple arithmetic, we can easily calculate what fraction of a horsepower will be delivered by any battery or cell. The unit of electric power is the watt. There are 746 watts in an electrical horsepower. Watts are arrived at by simply multiplying volts by amperes. As an instance, a battery delivering 20 amperes at 4½ volts *is capable* of producing 90 watts or nearly 1/7 of a horsepower. We must note that it was said that the battery *is capable*. The actual power delivered as measured in watts would depend upon the current consumed by the electrical apparatus connected to the battery. An electric heater might consume a great deal, a toy motor very little.

The useful life of a battery depends almost entirely upon how fast the current is consumed. Some electric cells are made in such a way that the metal element consumed by the chemical solution in the cell can be replaced with a fresh piece. This permits the student to salvage the unused parts.

Big adventures lie ahead. We are going to make a battery!

Chapter 4

WE MAKE A BATTERY

FORTUNATELY for young electricians with lean spending purses, electric cells may be made for a few pennies each and we may keep our little laboratory in an endless supply of current with little trouble. These batteries are reliable, easy to replenish and care for and they, unlike many chemical cells, do not involve highly corrosive and dangerous acids.

The boy who does have sufficient pocket money may, if he wishes, purchase two or three dry cells for a battery. With good care, these will last for a number of months. They will cost between fifty cents to a dollar each, depending on size. By good care we mean that the battery should not be permitted to stand in the hot sun or any highly heated place, it should be worked moderately and it should not be short-circuited (the positive or carbon pole of the battery should not be connected directly to the negative or zinc pole). In the case of a purchased dry cell, so much current will flow through a wire used to short-circuit it that it almost instantly heats to a point where one runs the risk of having one's fingers burned. Even an instant's short-circuiting will do great harm to a cell or battery and we resolve, as careful young electricians, not to abuse any battery in this way whether it is purchased or made at home.

Another curious thing about the type of cell being discussed is that heavy demands made upon it will bring quick but not permanent exhaustion. If such cells are permitted to rest for a period after a spell of hard work, they will regain their strength and become just as good as new, especially if they are "young." Therefore, should we, during one of our numerous experiments, find that our battery shows alarming signs of weakness, let us not make the mistake of putting it aside as permanently dead. As like as not it will be as fresh as a daisy in the morning.

This is due to a more or less strange phenomenon called "polarization" by the electrician.

For our homemade cells we shall need two or three one-quart fruit jars. If at all possible, it is better to build three cells than two. When we know how to do the trick, however, we may make as many as we wish.

The zinc needed for making wet cells may be obtained by reclaiming the zinc from old, worn-out dry cells, as explained later, or a few square feet of sheet zinc may be purchased at a sheet metal-working shop. Several square feet of sheet zinc can be bought for about one dollar. Two square feet will be sufficient to make four or five wet cells. Before it is used, the sheet zinc should be scrubbed thoroughly with soap and water to remove the grease left on at the rolling mill. The zinc and the solution used in the cells are the only things that will need replacement and replenishment.

How long the zinc lasts will depend upon how much the battery is used and how hard it is worked. Here it should be recalled that the zinc in an electric cell is something like the coal in a steam boiler. It is "burned up" to supply the electric energy. The faster the electricity is generated and used, the faster the zinc fuel in the cell or battery will be "burned."

It is quite possible that the young battery maker will not be able to obtain carbon rods at any local supply house. However, when ordinary dry cells become useless they are discarded and the carbon rods or poles in them may be removed. They are still just as good as the day they were set in place, although it would be best if we scraped them down and sandpapered them after they are removed. Millions of these cells are discarded every year and if we apply at a local telephone office or electrical dealer, it will not take long to discover a good reliable source.

Many dry cells are discarded long before all the zinc is consumed. In the case of the so-called dry cell, the container in which the active materials are placed is a zinc can and it is this that is consumed. But practically every dry cell that is thrown away has a great deal of useful zinc left in it and this zinc can be salvaged for use. We simply use a little care in breaking the container and removing the carbon rod and the active material. The partially destroyed zinc container is then cleaned as carefully as possible and set up in a fruit jar as shown in Fig. 2. It should be made clear that no other metal but zinc should be immersed in the solution.

The chemical needed for the active solution is a very common one and can usually be bought at a local

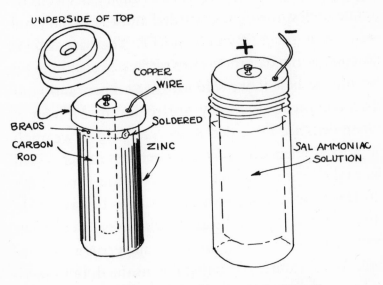

UNDERSIDE OF TOP

COPPER WIRE

BRADS

SOLDERED

CARBON ROD

ZINC

+   −

SAL AMMONIAC SOLUTION

Fig. 2. Mechanical details of the electric cell.

drugstore for a few cents a pound. Sal ammoniac is the chemical and it comes in granulated or powder form readily dissolving in water. Four ounces will be needed for each cell made and we should see to it that the chemical is thoroughly dissolved and that part of the powder does not finally come to rest in the bottom of the fruit jar. The dissolving of the sal ammoniac can be hastened by stirring the water and by heating it.

Immediately the elements or carbon and zinc poles are set in the solution, electric current can be generated if the circuit is completed. To test our battery, two copper wires are connected to it in the proper manner, as explained previously, and these are touched momentarily. An electric spark should be produced when this is done.

The young student of electricity will find that a battery of three cells will supply enough current for ordinary uses such as lighting miniature lamps, running toy motors and for many fascinating electromagnetic experiments that can be made. A three-cell battery will deliver 4½ volts and probably 10 to 30 amperes, depending upon the size of the zinc electrode and its general condition. At any rate, we shall have a very useful and faithful little powerhouse and we shall have the further satisfaction of having made it ourselves.

If new sheet zinc is used instead of reclaimed zinc from old dry cells, the builder can roll the zinc around

Fig. 3. The electric cell complete and ready for action.

a rolling pin to form a cylinder. As in the case of the reclaimed zinc cylinder, one end of this formed cylinder is nailed to the underside of the wooden top as illustrated in Fig. 2, page 28. Brass brads are used instead of ordinary nails.

Whether new sheet zinc or the zinc from an old dry cell is used, the carbon positive pole in a wet cell of this sort is always mounted in the center of the zinc cylinder.

Chapter 5

WE DISCOVER ELECTROMAGNETISM

THE curious relationship between electricity and magnetism is one of the great mysteries of science. Our scientists have discovered a great many laws governing the relationship but they are still pretty much in the dark about the real nature of the strange family ties. Under certain conditions, magnetism can be changed into electricity, but electricity in motion always generates magnetism.

It is fortunate indeed that the young student of electricity can, even with very simple and inexpensive apparatus, conduct many fascinating experiments in electromagnetism. If he wishes to reach out to the more simple textbooks after he completes the experiments that follow, he will find material and suggestions for new and exciting work that will keep him busy for months.

For our first experiment, we shall need a small, inexpensive pocket compass of the type carried by Boy Scouts. These are usually sold at the toy counters of the chain stores for about twenty-five cents. They are not only sensitive to the earth's magnetism but to magnetism from whatever source. Many young students will be surprised to learn that a bare compass can serve not only as a detector of magnetism but as a detector of electricity as well. Wherever electricity moves, magnetism follows along; it is the ever-present handmaiden of what we call "current" or "moving" electricity. As we walk about the streets of our town or city, our bodies are constantly passing through these invisible "magnetic fields" as they are called. Every power line and telephone wire generates them and spreads them far and wide.

The first experiment is simple enough and most interesting. If we had been the first to make it over a hundred years ago, we should have been credited with one of the most valuable discoveries of all time. As is the case with so many important discoveries, it was made quite accidentally. Hans Christian Oersted, a young Danish scientist, was lecturing before a group of students in Copenhagen. He was demonstrating one of Volta's famous Crown of Cups and happened to notice that when current flowed through a wire that passed near a compass on his lecture bench the needle of the compass moved violently. Oersted knew very well that ordinary magnets affected compass needles but he did not know that electricity could do the same thing. Experiments later performed by him showed that the electricity flowing in the wire was only indirectly responsible for the presence of the effect. Oersted was amazed to find that every wire carrying an electric current became a magnet whose power depended entirely upon the strength of the electric current passing through it. We can now duplicate this far-reaching and classical experiment with the very simple equipment that we have at hand.

The experiment (Fig. 4) can be set up in a minute or so. Two wires are connected to the battery, one to the positive (carbon) and one to the negative (zinc) pole. These wires should be long enough so that one may rest on the compass and run parallel to the needle. The bare ends of the wires are brought together mo-

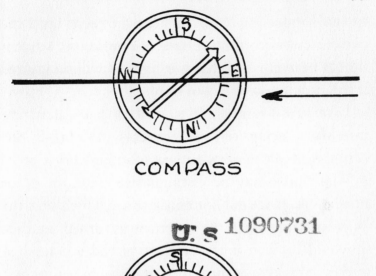

COMPASS

Fig. 4. How electric current flowing through a wire affects a compass needle. The direction of the movement of the needle is reversed when the current is reversed.

mentarily as we keep one eye on the compass needle. If the needle was pointing due north before the circuit was completed (all good compass needles should do this), it will instantly turn to a point at right angles to the conducting wire and remain there until the current ceases to flow. Here, of course, the student should bear in mind that our battery will be injured if the circuit is kept closed too long.

Like real scientists, it is well to keep alert and watchful during our experiments. Doubtless our compass needle is in two tones of color so that the S or south pole may be distinguished from the N or north pole. If we did not check to see which way the N pole swung when the current was turned on, then it would be well if the student placed a couple of staples or tacks over the wire that passes over the compass so that it cannot be drawn out of place. Our next experiment especially will need this sort of an arrangement.

The next piece of work simply amounts to changing or shifting the wires connected to the battery. The wire connected to the zinc or negative pole is shifted over to the carbon or positive pole and vice-versa. This is done to change the direction of the flow of the electricity in relation to the compass. Offhand, the young experimenter might consider this rather a silly thing to try but it turns out to have a rather important result.

Again keeping our eyes on the compass, we bring
the ends of the battery wires together once more.
Curiously enough, the compass needle again jumps,
but this time it turns in a direction opposite to that it
took the last time. Changing the direction of the
current has also changed the direction in which the
compass needle turns. Something has happened to the
strange and mysterious magnetic fingers reaching out
from the electric wire to pull the compass needle
around. First they tugged in one direction and then
they pulled in the opposite direction. Oersted found
this to be true also, and his learned writings on the
relationship between electricity and magnetism
brought him immortal fame.

With the simple equipment at hand, aided by a few
additional feet of copper wire, we can duplicate many
other classical experiments that were first performed
by the early masters. But first it will be interesting to
see what else may be done with the present compass
and battery.

After the compass is removed from beneath the
wire that passed over it, the experimenter may move
it farther and farther away from the wire carrying the
current to see how far the magnetism will reach out to

turn the compass needle. It will not take long to discover that, in the case of our little battery, the magnetic field becomes very weak after the compass has been moved a few inches. Indeed the strength of any magnetic field generated by electricity flowing through wires is in direct proportion to the strength of the electric current itself. Some currents used in industry are so powerful that they produce magnetic fields that may be detected by compasses over a distance of several hundred feet.

A short time after Oersted had published the results of his famous experiments, André Marie Ampère, a French scientist, began a series of investigations that soon proved to be of great importance. Here again the young experimenter can duplicate these now classical experiments.

Even before Oersted's time, it was known that the like poles of magnetic bodies (as $N + N$ or $S + S$) repelled each other and that dissimilar poles (as $S + N$) attracted each other. Now Ampère showed that magnetic fields generated by the flow of electricity through wires demonstrated the same peculiarity. To prove this, he took two fine wires and ran them side by side. He discovered, perhaps much to his surprise, that when current passed through the wires in the same direction, the wires repelled each other. On the other hand, when the current flowed in one direction in one wire and in the opposite direction in the other wire (see Fig. 5), the wires attracted each other. Under these conditions Ampère found that wires car-

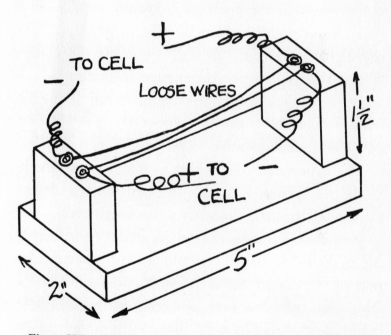

Fig. 5. Wires carrying electricity act in the manner of magnets. Electricity passing in the same direction in both causes repulsion. When passing in opposite directions, attraction between the wires is noticed.

rying electric current behaved like magnets. This turned out to be a very important discovery, and our engineers make wide use of it today.

If we have some tinsel or fine metallic braid such as that sold at the notions counter of a department store, we may set up the apparatus shown in Fig. 5. It will be noticed that the conductors are mounted so that they droop slightly. They should be placed within one-eighth of an inch of each other. If the equipment is set up properly, the current from a single cell should be sufficient for the demonstration. Thus the battery may be broken up temporarily and the two cells used independently.

The experimenter will have to watch very closely while the current is passing through the wires if he is to notice the marvelous effect that is achieved.

Ampère further discovered that coils of wire carrying electricity behaved very much as permanent magnets of steel. They, too, had north and south poles. Not only that, but very powerful magnetic effects could be produced by coils. Since a magnetic field exists around a wire carrying electricity, it is evident that if the wire is wound into a coil the result will be a concentration of the magnetism. This principle is used a great deal today in the design of electrical machinery. Indeed, if it were not for this, we would have no electric motors, dynamos, or transformers or any of the many and sundry electrical devices employed in the home and in industry.

Anyone who has not made an electric coil cannot be called an amateur electrician, so we are going to set about making a coil, called a solenoid. This is rather a strange name for a very simple device. We simply use the empty metal spool supplied with medical adhesive tape. This should be of the smallest size and should be wound full of copper wire. The experimenter will understand that this copper wire must be insulated; that is, covered with rubber, silk or cotton so that one turn of wire will not touch (electrically) the next turn. What we need in particular for this solenoid of ours (see Fig. 6) is the kind of wire found on the coil of an electric doorbell. Only a few feet are needed and any electrical shop can supply some new wire. If they do not have it in stock, then it may be taken from a burned-out coil of some kind. Electrical shops have any amount of wire in this form. We ask for ¼ pound of magnet wire, either 18, 20, 22 or 24 gage. Any form of insulation will do.

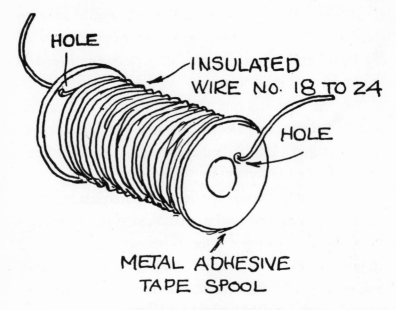

Fig. 6. A powerful electric solenoid may be made by winding an adhesive tape spool full of bell wire.

In making our coil or solenoid, it will be well to shellac or varnish each layer of wire as it is put into place so that the little device will hold together better.

Each coating of shellac or varnish should be allowed to dry before another layer of wire is wound in place. Plenty of shellac or varnish should be used on each layer. Make the solenoid about 2 or 2½ inches long and wind on four or five layers of wire. Be sure the turns of wire are placed as close to each other as possible and that all kinks are removed from the wire before it is wound in place. Should the experimenter have plenty of wire at hand, it will be advisable to wind two coils since many extra stunts can be performed with two.

Our first experiment using the coil is that of inducing or creating magnetism in a piece of steel by the aid of the coil. (See Fig. 7.) When electricity passes

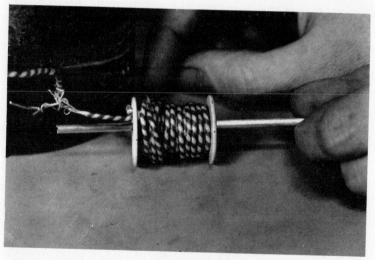

Fig. 7. A piece of steel will be magnetized when it is placed in the center of a coil carrying electric current from a battery.

through this coil or solenoid from the battery, the invisible magnetism not only surrounds the coil, but it also exists in the center of the coil. Oddly enough, when metals such as iron or steel are placed inside the coil while the current is on, they share this magnetism. First, we insert a nail and we note that as long as current passes through the coil the nail will attract and hold other nails. However, when the current is cut off, the nail loses most of its magnetism. It may not have enough left to attract other nails, but if it is brought near the compass, the needle will swing either toward it or away from it because the nail will now have an N and an S pole even though it is only slightly magnetized. Should the N pole of the nail (magnet) be brought nearest the N pole of the compass needle (also a magnet) then repulsion will take place.

The amount of magnetism retained by a piece of iron or steel will depend largely upon the power of the magnetizing current and upon the grade of the steel or iron. Very soft iron or pure iron will hold very little. Steel, on the other hand, will hold a great deal. We noted that once the flow of current was stopped, a magnetized nail did not retain enough magnetic power to lift another nail. But when a steel darning needle is magnetized by the solenoid, it will be found that it holds most of its magnetism, and that for periods as long as several years it is capable of lifting other needles. If the experimenter has little rods of steel that will fit inside the solenoid, he may engage in the manufacture of magnets with his simple equipment.

In magnetizing needles and little pieces of steel with our magnetizer coil, the current should not be permitted to flow through the coil from the battery for more than a few seconds. This will be quite sufficient. Longer exposure will not necessarily increase the degree of magnetism held by the steel.

Some time back the young electrical worker was cautioned against short-circuiting his battery and individual cells for any great length of time. This is wasteful not only of energy but also of materials. The zinc in cells is consumed at a very high rate when this is done and cells so treated will not last very long.

The inquiring mind is bound to ask why this should be so. The answer is: because there is nothing to stop the flow of electrical current; it just goes on as fast as the battery or cell can produce it. At this point we should consider the matter of resistance; electrical resistance, that is. If a coil of wire having high electrical resistance is connected to our battery, then very little current will flow and one will not need to be so careful about the length of time the coil is left in the circuit with the current on. The little magnetizer coil just completed does not have a very high electrical resistance, but it can still be left connected to the battery for a few seconds without causing any real harm. On the other hand, a small toy electric motor can be operated by the battery for a considerable length of time without doing any damage. Some electrical devices could be left in the circuit for many hours without draining the battery. Different things consume electricity at different rates.

Should the young worker have a toy horseshoe magnet at hand, a most interesting experiment can be made. Reference is made to Fig. 8. Here it will be seen that the magnetizing coil is suspended by means of two wires and that it is more or less free to move. We then permit current from the battery to pass through the coil and at the same time bring one pole of the horseshoe magnet near the free end of the coil. The coil is either attracted by the magnet or repelled by it, depending upon the direction in which the current is

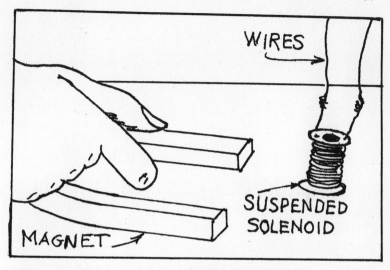

Fig. 8. A suspended coil or solenoid carrying electric current will act as a magnet and can be repelled or attracted in the manner illustrated.

passing through the coil. Should one pole of the magnet attract the end of the coil, the other pole of the magnet will repel it.

Many fascinating hours can be spent with this simple equipment and our young friends will be amazed at our knowledge of the mysterious force of electricity.

Chapter 6

A MAGIC CURRENT DETECTOR

MANY ingenious devices have been made to detect and measure electric current. Some will measure as little as one millionth of an ampere. While we cannot hope to match such wonderful instruments, we can, aided by our compass, build a simple little machine that will produce marvelous results and that will permit us to carry on our electrical work with greater promise of learning more and having more fun at the same time. No more than an hour or so will be needed for the construction, and the materials required will cost very little.

Figures 9 and 10 will present the details. The block should be cut from hard wood if possible to prevent splitting. The grooves for the wire are cut with a saw and chisel. If a hacksaw is at hand, this will do nicely

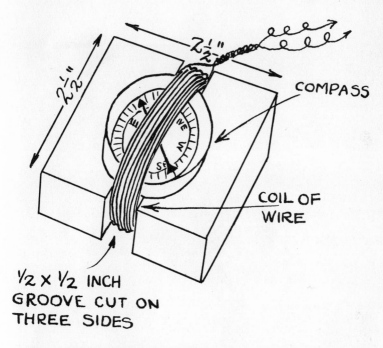

Fig. 9. The dimensions and general construction features of the compass current detector.

for cutting the wood because it will make a fine cut. The wood between the saw cuts is removed with a sharp chisel. Dad's assistance at this point might be most welcome but, if it cannot be had, there is no reason why any boy with average skill in handling tools cannot do the trick.

Fig. 10. The completed magic current detector ready for use.

After the groove has been cut, the wood is sandpapered and then varnished or shellacked. Now the block is ready for wiring. We can use the same type of wire that we used in making the solenoid described in the preceding chapter.

The compass is set in place as shown in the drawing and photograph, and then about twenty turns of wire are wound around the compass and in the grooves. This holds the compass in place. Several inches of wire are left free at both ends and wound around each other—see Fig. 10—to form the connectors. The instrument is completed by giving it another coat of shellac or varnish, wire and all. When this is dry, the current detector will be ready for use.

When a battery or cell is momentarily connected to the current detector, we note that the compass needle is violently turned one way or another, depending upon the direction taken by the current. This can be quickly checked by shifting the wires coming from the cell or battery.

The instrument does not need the current from a cell or battery to make the needle of the compass move. It is much more sensitive than that as we shall very soon see.

When the magnetizing coil was wound, it was suggested then that it might be well to wind two such coils because the time would come when experimental

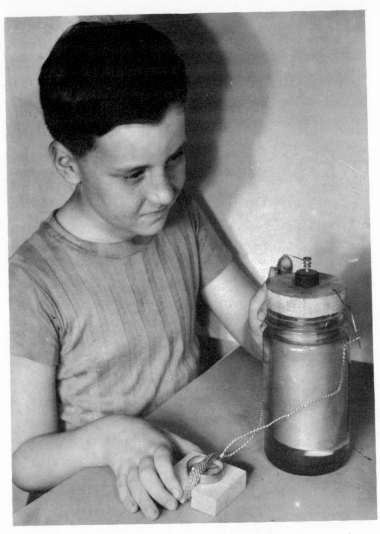

Fig. 11. The current detector being used to test an electric cell.

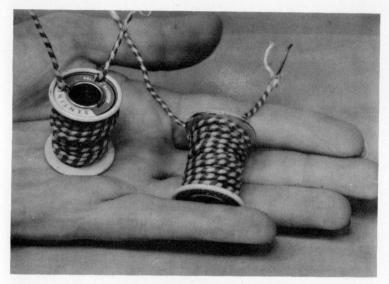

Fig. 12. The two solenoids used in the experiments with magnetism.

work would require an extra one. We have now reached that stage. We are about ready to show how electricity can jump from one coil to another so if we have not already wound a second coil, we shall have to take time out until this is done.

The second coil is connected directly to the current detector as shown in Fig. 13. Both coils are then set side by side and the wires leading from the second coil are connected directly to the cell or battery. As

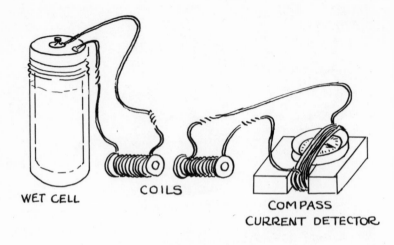

WET CELL   COILS   COMPASS
                                 CURRENT DETECTOR

Fig. 13. The electrical connections in the jumping-current
experiment.

this is done, the worker keeps his eye on the compass
needle of the magic current detector. Sure enough, it
jumps into action, although the electric circuit of
which it forms a part is not connected in any way to
the circuit containing the battery and coil.

Actually, the electricity jumped from one circuit
to the other and the inquisitive boy will want to know
something about the method. Of course, there is a
great deal of mystery about it. Even the great scientists do not know the whole story, but the laws gov-

erning this wonderful transfer of electrical energy across space are known.

The close relationship between electricity and magnetism has already been commented upon. We know that electricity can produce magnetism, but did we know that magnetism can produce electricity? Probably not, because the discovery cannot be made without a current detector such as we have just placed in service.

It will be clear that the electric current from the battery will generate a magnetic force or field around the first coil when electricity from the battery flows through it. This point has already been covered. When this magnetic force reaches out from the first coil to touch the second coil near by, a momentary current of electricity is generated in the second coil and a flicker of the needle is seen. But why, we rightfully ask, does the current flow for only a tiny fraction of a second?

The story of that goes back a long way to Michael Faraday, once called the Prince of Experimenters. It was during the year 1837 that this great man, who with only self-education became one of the greatest figures of science, discovered electromagnetic induction. We should be thrilled to find that we have just performed one of his greatest experiments. Were it not for the principle of electromagnetic induction, the electrical world as we know it today could not exist.

Faraday found among many other things that electricity could not be generated by electromagnetic forces until either the magnetic lines of force themselves moved or the coil in which the current was to be generated moved. It is easy to check these findings, and we shall then be able to understand why there was but a momentary current in the second or detector circuit when electricity passed through the coil connected to the battery.

These magnetic fields generated by electricity passing through coils, unlike the permanent and stable fields produced by steel magnets, start weakly and then spread out from the coil with a sort of expanding effect. While this is taking place, of course, the mysterious and invisible lines of force are actually moving outward and for that reason current is produced in the second coil. Just as soon as the lines of magnetic force generated by the electricity flowing through the first coil reach their limit, they remain motionless.

Therefore no more current will be produced in the second circuit.

The young worker can immediately check this theory and quickly satisfy himself that it is a fact indeed. While the current is passing through the first coil connected to the battery, he suddenly moves it, keeping his eye on the needle of the current detector. Sure enough, the needle will move every time either one of the coils is moved. This rule may then be set down: electromagnetic induction of electric currents takes place only when either the coils or the magnetic field is moved.

Another check can be made by repeated completing and breaking of the circuit containing the battery and the coil. Every time this is done, the needle of the compass will jiggle. It would appear that electric current is really jumping across space in a radio-like manner. It is in a sense, but only through the agency of the strange force of magnetism.

As in the case of electricity some things conduct magnetism better than others. Soft iron, for instance, conducts magnetism better than any other material. Steel, too, is a good conductor, much better than air. This point can be proven by a simple experiment.

The two coils that we have been using are slipped over a small iron bolt, and the last experiment is tried again. Careful observation of the compass needle should show that it responds with greater movement than before when the current first flows from the battery through the first coil. This is so because the iron bolt conducts magnetism much better than does air.

The last experiment demonstrated the principle of the electric transformer. A transformer is a device for changing the voltage and amperage of alternating current (A.C.) electricity. We have been dealing only with direct current (D.C.) electricity. All batteries or cells generate only pure direct current. When transformers are used to increase the voltage of alternating current, they are called "step-up" transformers. When they are used to decrease the voltage and increase the current (amperage), they are called "step-down" transformers.

Transformers are never used with direct current for the simple reason that they will not work. We noticed that current flowed in the second circuit only at the instant of contact in the first circuit containing the battery. Again it is stated that magnetic fields produced by electricity must be made to move if current is to be induced in other circuits through electromagnetic induction.

Transformers operate on alternating current because this kind of current is constantly changing its direction of flow and to change its direction of flow it must fall to zero each time. Thus in effect no alternating current flows for a tiny fraction of a second while reversal is taking place. This has the same effect as turning the current off. We noted during our experiment that the compass needle could be kept in a state of practically constant movement as long as the contact in the battery circuit was rapidly broken and remade.

The transformer is one of the most widely used electrical devices. Without it electricity could not be sent over long distances and the home use of electrical equipment would be highly impractical.

Returning for a moment to our last experiment, we noted that we had two separate electric circuits. One contained the battery and the coil and the other held a coil and a compass. The only path between the two was magnetic rather than electric. Every transformer used on alternating current has two circuits also. The circuit where the current enters (equivalent to our battery circuit) is called the "primary circuit." The circuit where it leaves is called the "secondary circuit." Thus in the case of our last experiment, the first coil would be called the primary and the second coil the secondary. The connecting link of iron would be called the "core" of the transformer. The cores of most alternating-current transformers are built like square doughnuts with coils wound at opposite ends and sometimes over each other.

As fascinating as this alternating current business is, we had better return to our little battery. With it we may come to master the great principles of electricity as they were discovered by the pioneers. With these great fundamentals or "first things" set in mind, one can be prepared to make rapid progress in the study of electricity.

A small quantity of iron filings will be needed for the next experiment. They are obtained by filing a piece of soft iron, such as might be found in a casting, with a coarse file. The article to be filed is placed in a vise with a piece of paper beneath it to catch the iron particles as they fall. Work is continued until about a thimbleful of the powdered metal is produced.

Magnetic lines of force may be visualized by the

use of these filings. As an example, a piece of heavy paper is laid over a horseshoe or bar magnet, and iron filings are carefully sprinkled over the paper. Much to our astonishment, the tiny particles line up in a definite pattern; they actually follow the so-called

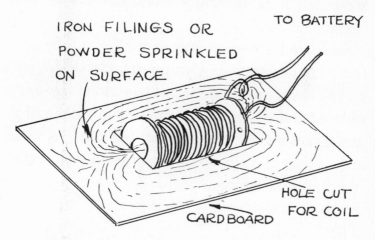

Fig. 14. How the magnetic lines of force generated by current passing through a coil can be visualized by the use of fine iron filings.

"magnetic lines of force" produced by the magnet. It is found that these lines of force are greatest near the poles or ends of the magnet and least near the center or midway point.

Curiously enough, the magnetic lines of force of

a coil of wire can also be traced with the aid of iron filings. The coil is arranged as seen in Fig. 14. The filings are sprinkled over the cardboard as evenly as possible, and current is sent through the coil. Just as in the case of the steel magnet, this electromagnet, as it is called in the workaday world of electricity, also has its poles.

So much for these strange cousins of science, electricity and magnetism. Our program from this point on will be devoted to the use of our knowledge gained thus far and to the construction of devices and the performance of experiments that will carry us farther and farther into the wonderland of one of nature's most marvelous forces.

Chapter 7

THE MAGNETIC DIVER

OUR project is a simple one, but it offers much fun not only for ourselves but for our friends as well, who will marvel at it. The materials are simple enough: a bit of wire, a small piece of wood and a small glass phial which can be bought at the drugstore for under ten cents.

A piece of wood about three inches square and one inch thick is cut first. This serves as the base of the device.

The copper wire used may be reclaimed either from electric doorbell or buzzer coils or it may be purchased from the electrical supply counter at the local five-and-ten-cent store. It should not be over

No. 18 or under No. 22 in size and it should be covered with some sort of insulation.

About six or seven feet of this wire must be wound around the middle of the glass phial and this will not be easy unless the glass surface is prepared in some manner. Therefore, a bit of shellac is used to cover the area and the wire is wound in place while this is still tacky. This prevents the wire from slipping off. Another and perhaps better way is to shellac the area and then wind a piece of paper over the partially dried coating. The wire can be made to remain in place over the paper. Added security will be insured if the wire is given a good heavy coat of shellac after it has been set in place.

Two pigtails should be left on the coil, these to serve as terminals for the instrument.

After the shellac on the coil has set, the phial is cemented to the center of the baseboard. This done, fill the phial with water. Now drive a tack into a small piece of cork and put this into the phial. The piece of cork must be just large enough to keep itself and the tack afloat. Therefore the cork should be cut away, a small piece at a time, until this point is reached. Then,

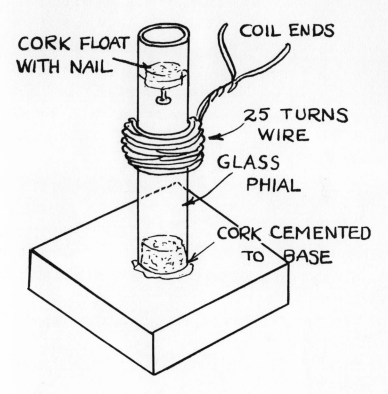

CORK FLOAT WITH NAIL

COIL ENDS

25 TURNS WIRE

GLASS PHIAL

CORK CEMENTED TO BASE

Fig. 15. The construction details of the strange magnetic diving device.

when current from the battery is passed through the coil wound around the middle of the glass phial, the cork and the tack will plunge downward and disappear only to bob upward and remain afloat once the

Fig. 16. The magnetic diver ready for use.

current is cut off. The current should not be left on more than a few seconds at a time if our battery is to enjoy a long and useful life.

We can also make a magnetic boat with our phial device. Cement a piece of a broken steel needle to a bit of cork (smaller than the piece we used before) or a sliver of wood. Then remove some of the water in the phial, insert the cork or wooden boat, and stop up the open end of the phial with a cork. Place the phial on its side. The little boat will sail away to the center of the coil when electric current from a cell or battery passes through it.

Chapter 8

GAS FROM ELECTRICITY

As THE young student progresses with his study of electricity, he will reach a point where he finds it difficult to separate this strange force from the world at large. It appears to be everywhere, in the earth, in the clouds, in the human body and in all and sundry things. What is more, there is a curious and close relationship between chemistry and electricity just as there is between magnetism and electricity. Indeed, our battery operates on an electrochemical principle. The zinc is consumed chemically and in so passing it generates electric current just as heat is created when coal is burned.

Some time ago it was pointed out that magnetism

can generate electricity and also that electricity can generate magnetism. We now know that chemical action can produce electricity, but we shall perhaps be surprised to learn that electricity can produce chemical action. The more we experiment with electricity the more we see that there is a very close relationship between chemistry, electricity and magnetism. In some cases, all three are busy at the same time. Such an instance can be made the subject of a very pretty experiment.

A drinking glass is half filled with water and two wires from the battery are immersed in it. If the water is pure, very little will happen. Pure water is a very poor conductor of electricity indeed. Should it be exceptionally pure, it will conduct hardly at all. However, if we drop a couple of spoonfuls of acetic acid (vinegar) into the glass containing the water and then immerse the two bare wires, a very lively chemical action will take place. Gas bubbles galore form about the ends of the wires and quickly rush to the surface of the solution and escape into the atmosphere. They proceed in endless streams and continue to form as long as the current flows.

This experiment should form a hallowed moment

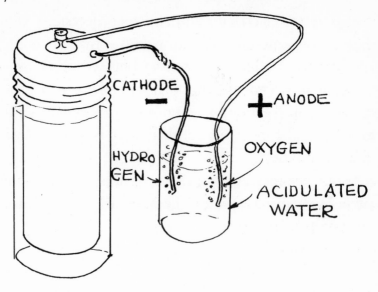

Fig. 17. How electricity can be made to generate the gases hydrogen and oxygen when it passes through acidulated water.

in the life of any young scientist. Our thoughts drift back over a hundred years to a young man at work in the laboratories of the Royal Institute in London, England. He, too, is watching bubbles proceed from two small connectors (electrodes) that he has immersed in acidulated water. A large part of the fame that came to him later was based on that part of his work dealing with the tie between chemistry and electricity. The man was Michael Faraday, one of the most imaginative and accomplished experimenters of all time.

What we witnessed, more or less idly perhaps, in the preceding experiment is the important action called electrolysis. As we read this, thousands upon thousands of electrochemical cells are busy in our country creating elements and compounds through the agency of electricity. Faraday, and Sir Humphry Davy before him, blazed the trail that later formed the basis of our great electrochemical industry.

The boy with any curiosity at all will not be able to rest until he knows something more about this marvelous experiment. What are these gases and why do they issue?

When acidulated water (that is, water mixed with any acid) is electrolyzed (that is, when electricity is permitted to pass through it), the water is always decomposed or broken down into its constituent elements, as the chemist would say. Early experimenters in electricity placed two glass test tubes over the electrodes or connectors in the acid solution, and in place of escaping into the surrounding air, the gases were imprisoned in the tubes. In every instance and no matter what acid was used to make the solution, it was found that hydrogen and oxygen were formed. These are the gases that go to make up water, which has the formula H_2O, where the H_2 stands for hydrogen and the O for oxygen. Here, then, before our very eyes, water is being destroyed by the aid of electric current. The greater the amount of electricity used, the greater the amount of gases generated.

There are many wonders in electrochemistry and there is at least one more experiment that we shall want to make before we pass on to other exciting work. It is to be shown that a solution of a compound of the metal element copper can be broken down by electric current to liberate the copper metal.

A few ounces of the compound called copper sulphate or blue vitriol is purchased at the corner drugstore. A couple of teaspoonfuls are dissolved in a glass of water. If the water is heated a bit, the blue crystals will be dissolved much faster.

This done, we scurry around and find a little piece of brass and a little piece of copper. Neither piece needs to be over an inch square. Both pieces are washed in warm water with plenty of soap and carefully rinsed off with clean water to make sure that every trace of dirt has been removed. It is very important that these metals, especially the piece of brass, be very clean. Now for the fun and the surprise!

The pieces of brass and copper are attached to two pieces of copper wire and immersed in the copper sulphate solution. Then the wire leading from the piece of brass is connected to the negative or zinc pole of the battery and the wire attached to the piece of copper is connected to the positive or carbon pole.

Immediately these electrical connections have been completed and electric current begins to flow, things begin to happen and we should keep a close watch on the piece of brass. Nothing visible occurs for a few seconds, but finally it will be noted that the color of the piece of brass is beginning to change. It becomes a soft, salmon-like pink. This will gradually darken into a pure copper color.

Here the action of the electricity is separating the copper from the solution of copper sulphate and causing the copper to be deposited on the surface of the piece of brass. It is all very wonderful. If the brass has been well cleaned before it was placed in the bath, there is little reason why the copper plated on its surface should not remain there for a long time.

Fig. 18. Small brass objects can be electroplated with copper with this simple equipment.

Aside from demonstrating one of the most interesting laws of electrochemistry, this simple but beautiful experiment also demonstrates the principle involved in electroplating.

Chapter 9

A FUSE IS BLOWN!

THE fuse is one of the simplest electrical devices in use and yet few of us know a great deal about it. The house lights go out, Father runs downstairs to replace a blown fuse and, presto! the lights are back on again. It is very mysterious. What are fuses and why should they blow?

Of course, fuses don't really blow; they melt, and they do this so quickly as to cause a small explosion. All of us must know that a water pipe will burst if it is called upon to carry too much water at too high a pressure. So it is with a fuse. Should too much electricity pass—that is, too many amperes—the tiny fuse wire through which it passes will become heated and, being formed of an alloy of metals that melt at a low temperature, the wire will eventually melt. This it does quickly, in a fraction of a second.

Electricity is a strange thing. When it goes on a rampage it never knows when to stop. It will heat even copper wires until they melt. It will burn out motors, start fires and raise Cain in general. Fuses and things called "circuit breakers" prevent such violent actions. Actually a fuse is a circuit breaker or a very simple automatic switch. When the wire in the fuse melts due to the passage of too much electricity, the electrical circuit is broken and electricity thereafter ceases to flow. The circuit is said to be "open" and the flow of current will not be re-established until the old fuse is removed and a new one set in its place.

Each fuse is rated on the basis of the number of amperes it will safely carry. Examination of the fuses on the electrical counter will show that some are marked 5, some 10 and some 20 and 25. This is in terms of amperes. This means that at a voltage of 110, a certain sized piece of fusible wire has been made that will carry only 5, 10, 20 or 25 amperes as the case may be. Should a large motor consuming 10 amperes of current be connected to a circuit protected with only a 5-ampere fuse, the fuse would blow instantly the motor was plugged in.

Copper electric wires are also made to pass only a certain amount of current at a certain voltage. If they are overloaded, they overheat and a dangerous situation arises. Hot wires conduct electricity less efficiently than cold wires and this alone generates more heat. Thus, one condition produces another until great damage is done.

The electrical fuse, then, is purely an electricity stopper, and we are going to set up an experiment that will prove this point. The arrangement used is shown in Fig. 19. Here the fuse element itself is formed by a tiny strip of tin (not aluminum) foil. This need not be more than 1/16th of an inch wide. It may be threaded through two paper clips, as in the illustration, to make the connection. The complete set of connections is shown in Fig. 20. To reach the light (it might be a motor or a bell) the electricity must first pass through the fuse.

Now let us directly and with malice aforethought commit an electrical outrage. We are going to cause

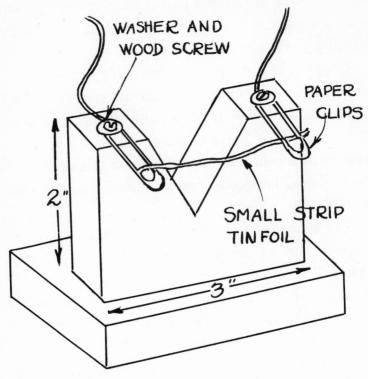

Fig. 19. How the fuse is held between paper clips.

a short circuit. To do this the two pieces of wire marked *x* and *x* in Fig. 21 are brought together as shown.

Electricity, like water running down a hill, always takes the shortest available path. Hence, when the

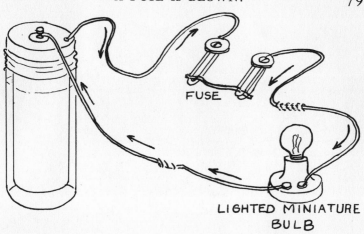

FUSE

LIGHTED MINIATURE
BULB

Fig. 20. How the fuse is connected to the electric circuit.

bared wires make contact, the current will no longer flow through the full length of wire. Rather, it will take the short cut or the *short circuit*. Here, having nothing else to do, it spends itself heating the circuit through which it flows. The little piece of tin foil forms part of the circuit and, keeping our eyes at a safe distance, we watch the fuse until it melts. This it does quickly once the short circuit is produced. There is a tiny flash and the tin foil melts down.

It is easy to understand, then, why electric circuits are protected by tiny pieces of metal that melt before the copper wires of the circuit can become over-

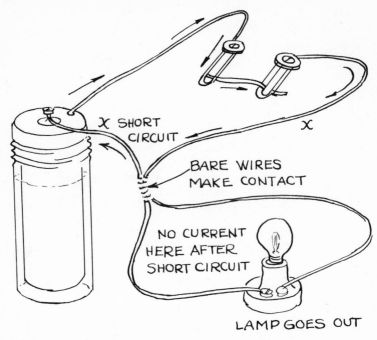

Fig. 21. The short circuit is created at the point where the bare wires meet. The lamp goes out and all of the current from the cell passes through the fuse, melting it.

heated. Fuses are like little sentinels that stand guard over electric circuits to say "You cannot pass" when electric currents start out on the rampage.

Chapter 10

TURNING DETECTIVE WITH A MICROPHONE

IF the young electrician can beg or borrow a single telephone receiver, he can set up a supersensitive microphone with which he may listen to the footfall of flies, hear sounds through thick walls and do all sorts of interesting things relating to the detection of small acoustic disturbances.

But, first, how does a microphone work? Actually, it is one of the simplest of electrical devices, especially in the form in which we shall be making it. A microphone is merely an electrical device built around a loose contact. By this we mean that the contact established between two or more carbon pieces (carbon conducts electric current rather well) is loose enough to respond to vibration, and this vibration at the contacting surface interferes more or less with the flow of current. Thus the current flowing in a microphone circuit will faithfully follow the intensity of the sound causing the vibration. When used with a telephone receiver, which is also one of the most sensitive current detectors known to science, the combination becomes a powerful instrument for the amplification of sound effects.

The materials required for our supersensitive microphone may be garnered from sources within easy reach and they should cost us precisely nothing. First we need a lead pencil. This so-called "lead" is really a comparatively pure form of carbon. A piece of lead about two and a half inches long will be needed.

The little carbon blocks noted in the illustrations of the microphone (see Figs. 22 and 23) are not so easily procured, although, if the worst comes to the worst, we can cut a small piece off the end of each one of the carbon rods in our electric cells. This will cause practically no damage. Indeed, it will never be missed. Oftentimes electric-motor repair shops discard worn-out carbon brushes that have been removed from electric motors. A serious young electrician can always have these for the asking if he presents his case nicely.

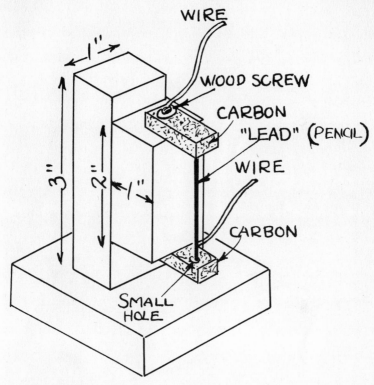

Fig. 22. The construction details of the microphone.

In working with carbon, the mechanic must be careful, because it is very brittle and breaks easily.

Hence, when the holes are drilled in the carbon blocks for the holding terminals, the worker must proceed carefully.

Fig. 23. The completed microphone.

The hole in each of the carbon blocks serves two purposes. A wood screw is used to hold the blocks in place and electrical connection is established with the blocks by placing a bare copper wire under the head of the screw before it is driven home. Here again the greatest care must be exercised. Otherwise the blocks will crack under pressure from the screw.

Before this final operation is entered into, the worker should drill a dimple in each carbon block so that the ends of the lead rod rest in them after the microphone is assembled. Before the rod is set in place, its ends should be carefully sharpened on a piece of fine sandpaper.

The dimensions given in the drawing should be followed as closely as possible to insure there is a loose connection between the ends of the rod and the blocks. If the rod is pinched in between the blocks and is not free to move slightly, the device will not function. Should this happen, then one of the blocks will have to be removed, the carbon rod filed away a bit more and the device reassembled.

One or two cells may be used for operating the microphone. It will be noted from Fig. 24 that the electrical connections for the equipment are quite simple. Once they are made, the operator can pick up the receiver and the detector will be instantly in

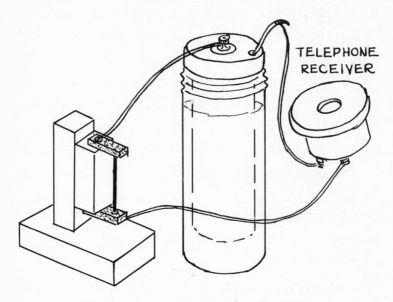

Fig. 24. Connections for the microphone.

use. If a watch is placed on the table near the "mike," the ticks should be clearly heard through the receiver. Sometimes improved sensitivity can be obtained if the carbon rod is turned with the fingers. Oftentimes an especially sensitive spot is found.

Much fun can be had with this mike in playing detective. It is simply pressed against the outer wall

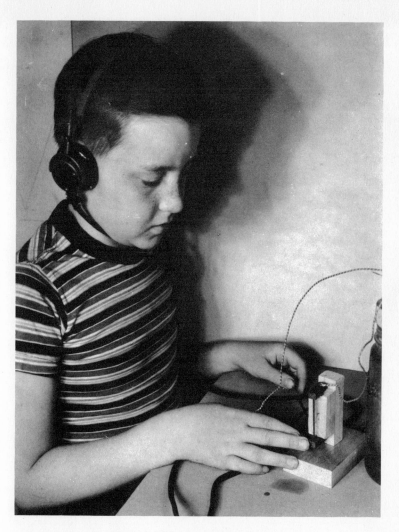

Fig. 25. The microphone in use.

of a room in which other members of the family are holding a conversation. If the apparatus has been made right, the conversation should be audible through the receiver.

Chapter 11

MAGIC ELECTRIC WRITING

WE have said that most things conduct electricity. Of course, if the voltage or pressure of the electricity is high enough, a tiny bit may be forced through glass or other insulating or nonconducting material. When such conduction takes place where high voltage is passing, it is said that some of the electricity leaks away.

Most liquids, unlike most solids, turn out to be pretty good conductors of electric current. Water is ordinarily looked upon as a good conductor of electricity, although it is not quite so good as most people think. It is not so good as even the poorest of metal conductors, such as German silver or iron. Indeed, chemically pure water, or water from which all foreign matter has been removed, turns out to be a very poor conductor of electricity, and at the lower voltages, it will not conduct at all. Mineral matter dissolved in water makes an excellent carrier of it.

Most chemicals that will dissolve in water greatly increase its conductivity. Furthermore, some materials, especially certain gases and metals, can be removed from water quickly in great quantities by the simple trick of passing electric current through the solution. A great industry has been founded on this simple principle. At Niagara Falls there are enormous electrochemical plants engaged in the manufacture or recovery of specific materials such as chlorine, sodium, oxygen, hydrogen, etc. This work is carried on in a closed vessel or cell into which electric current generated by the great cataract is permitted to flow.

In some cases, as, for instance, when electric current is permitted to pass through a solution of ordinary table salt dissolved in water, a gas is formed at one electrode and a metal at the other. (Electrodes are the conductors in contact with the solution through which the electricity flows in and out. The electrode through which the current enters the solution is called the "cathode." The one through which it leaves is called the "anode.") The gas is chlorine and the metal is sodium. This particular combination of the gas and the metal is known as sodium chloride and it has the chemical formula of NaCl, Na standing for the metal sodium and Cl for the gas chlorine.

Electricity, we find, is a chemical wrecker. When permitted to flow through many chemical compounds that are able to conduct it, it works many changes. This is especially true of chemical solutions formed in water. When a current brings about such changes, the process is referred to as electrolysis and the solution through which the electricity flows is called the electrolyte.

This conduction of electricity through chemical baths or electrolytes can be turned to good account in producing a stunt to amaze our friends. We shall call it electric writing, and shall write with "electric ink," using an "electric pencil." This is a trick which will mystify those who are not in on the secret.

We must ask our local druggist to supply us with about twenty-five cents' worth of a chemical called potassium iodide, the drug commonly taken for hardening of the arteries. This comes in a white crystalline form and a spoonful of it is dissolved in about a half glass of water. A perfectly colorless solution will result. Indeed, one would think that the solution was ordinary water, and to heighten the effects of our magic, we should not make a point of supplying information to the contrary.

After the potassium iodide has been completely dissolved, a small piece of porous paper, such as that used in mimeographing, is soaked in it and the excess moisture is allowed to drain off. Now the soaked paper is placed on a sheet of steel or any other metal, and this metal is connected to the battery. The other connection from the battery, which should be a copper wire, serves as the "pencil." If the connections are right, a sharp brown dot should be made upon the paper when the pencil wire touches it. If a dot is not made, then the connections from the battery should be reversed. This done, a deep reddish-brown line will be traced as we write slowly with the magic copper pencil.

Why the reddish-brown line? The potassium iodide (KI) is broken down into its constituent elements, potassium, the metal, collecting at one electrode and iodine at the other. What we are really

doing is writing with the iodine. The potassium col-
lects at the other electrode, but instantly it reaches
the metallic state, it enters into a vigorous chemical
reaction with the water present to form potassium
hydroxide or KOH, which takes its place as a colorless material in the water.

Chapter 12

MAKING A MOTOR IS FUN!

MAKE a motor? Many of us will think that the making of an electric motor would be too complicated and would require too many hard-to-get materials. *Not so!* No matter how modest our home workshop may be, it will yield the materials necessary for a practical, operating motor, and only an hour or so of our time will be required to set it a-humming on the bench.

The revolving part of a motor is called an armature. In our motor the armature is made with either a cork or a round piece of wood about 1 inch in diameter and ¾ of an inch thick. The cork or piece of wood is divided into six equal parts, which means that a mark must be made at every 60° if a protractor is used for this purpose. If we do not have such an instrument at home, a teacher at school will probably be glad to mark out the armature in this manner. The marking must be done accurately, otherwise the piece will be badly out of balance when it rotates and it is very apt to wobble, a performance that would set us down as bad workmen.

The shaft of the armature is made with a tenpenny nail. This is first prepared by sawing or filing off the head. Then a file is used to sharpen the pointed end. This end forms the lower bearing of the motor and the sharper and smoother it is, the better.

A hole slightly smaller than the nail is drilled through the center of the armature and we then drive six small nails into it at the places marked off. These nails must protrude exactly ⅝ of an inch, and every effort should be made to drive them as accurately and as straight as possible. Much of the success of the motor depends upon the care with which this is done. The prepared tenpenny nail is now forced through the hole in the armature, and this completes this part of the assembly.

About 12 or 15 feet of wire are now measured

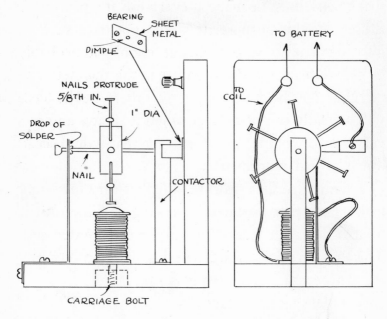

Fig. 26. General assembly of the various motor parts.

off, and this is wound around a heavy *iron* bolt placed upright in the motor frame so that the heads of the nails will just miss it when they whirl by on the armature. This is a case of the closer the better so long as they do not touch. The builder will now understand why care should be taken to see that the nails are driven in straight and at equal distances.

The bearing for the sharpened end of the armature

shaft is simple enough. A small piece of sheet tin plate, such as may be taken from a tin can, is fastened to the backboard of the frame with two small brads. After this is in place, a sharp instrument, such as a machinist's prick punch or a heavy needle, is used to form a dimple in the tin plate that will be just large enough for the sharp end of the armature shaft to fit into.

The metal holding piece at the front end of the baseboard is also made with sheet tin plate. A drop of solder should be put on the armature shaft behind this piece (see Fig. 26) to prevent the shaft from shifting horizontally as the armature of the motor revolves. Care should be taken to make sure the drop of solder is so placed that it will not cement the shaft to the metal strip but will be close enough to the strip to prevent the shaft from slipping.

Now the search will be on for a hexagon nut (that is a nut with six corners) to fit over the contactor end of the armature shaft. This should be soldered in place. Some of the liquid solder that can be applied without heat will do nicely.

The movable contactor device (see Figs. 26, 27 and 28) may also be cut from a discarded tin can.

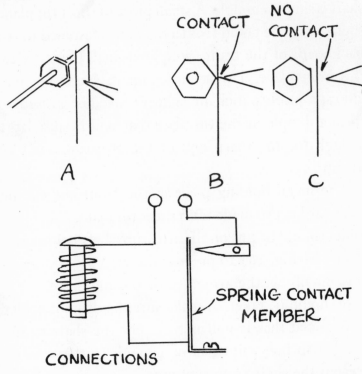

Fig. 27. The arrangement of the contact device and (lower) the diagram of connections for the motor.

This is made long so that it will bend easily. One end is fastened to the motor base with a wood screw and the other end is adjusted in such a manner that it will make contact with the six points of the hexagon nut as they whirl by. Not only must a contact be formed but the end of the long strip must be forced back in such a way that its opposite side will make electrical contact with a second piece of thin sheet metal attached to the backboard of the motor frame. It may be necessary to make a dimple in the end of the contactor strip so that it will protrude on the side opposite the nut. A better electrical connection will then be made when these parts contact during the operation of the motor.

The adjustment of this long contact member calls for patience on the part of the builder. The success or failure of our motor depends upon the precise adjustment of this part. Our motor will definitely operate, and at high speed, if the battery is strong enough, the connections are well and properly made and the *contactor functions properly*.

Every time one of the six points of the nut passes the strip, the latter should be moved outward to make contact with the stationary member. Naturally this, too, may be bent forward and backward to help in arriving at the right adjustment. When proper adjustment is achieved, the long strip should not touch either the flat side of the nut or the stationary member during the times the flat sides of the nut are

Fig. 28. The completed motor ready for action. The round black objects at the top are binding posts. The battery can be connected to two binding posts such as these or two small machine screws can be used. If the builder wishes, he can also make his battery connections direct. The binding posts or screws are not essential.

parallel with the long strip. This point will be clarified by reference to inserts B and C in Fig. 27.

We cannot expect an improvised motor of this kind to provide power for the operation of toys and the like. It is purely a demonstration machine intended to move its own armature only. After it has been connected, the armature is given a spin, and, if the contact member has been carefully set, the motor should continue to operate at high speed.

Chapter 13

HOW TO MAKE A
THERMOELECTRIC CELL

MANY years ago it was discovered that heat could be directly changed into electricity. It was during the year 1822 that a German physicist named Thomas Johann Seebeck discovered what is now called a thermoelectric cell, thermo meaning heat.

Seebeck found that when two dissimilar metals such as copper and zinc or iron and tin were brought into contact and the joint or union of the metals was heated, a small amount of electricity would be generated.

The amount of electricity generated depended

Fig. 29. A homemade thermoelectric cell that any young experimenter can make in a short time with very simple materials. Here the cell is connected to a current-measuring instrument. However, an old radio receiver may be used in place of this. Clicks in the receiver will prove that electricity is generated when a candle or a match is held beneath the junction of the two metals.

upon the amount of heat applied to the union, the size of the pieces of metal used and the nature of the metals, whether gold and silver or iron and tin, etc.

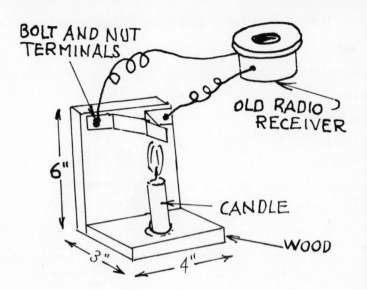

BOLT AND NUT TERMINALS

OLD RADIO RECEIVER

6"

CANDLE

WOOD

3"

4"

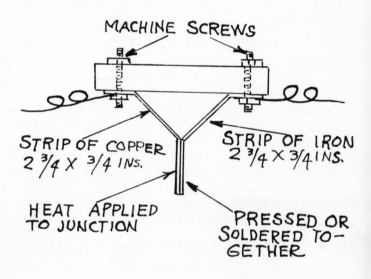

MACHINE SCREWS

STRIP OF COPPER
2 3/4 X 3/4 INS.

STRIP OF IRON
2 3/4 X 3/4 INS.

HEAT APPLIED
TO JUNCTION

PRESSED OR
SOLDERED TO-
GETHER

Great improvements in thermoelectric cells have been made during the past few years. In the near future perhaps much of the world's electricity may be generated in this fashion. No moving parts are needed in such generation.

The young experimenter can easily make a small thermoelectric cell. It will cost practically nothing. A photograph of the cell will be seen in Fig. 29. Fig. 30 shows the construction details.

While the cell is shown in the photograph with a galvanometer (current-measuring instrument), this does not need to be used. In its place the young experimenter may use a discarded radio headphone. One of these can usually be obtained from radio repairmen for the asking or at small cost. If this headphone receiver is connected to the thermoelectric cell while its metal elements are being heated, a distinct and loud

Fig. 30. (Left) The construction details of a simple thermoelectric cell. The detail at the bottom of this drawing shows how the pieces of metal are cut, bent and mounted. One is of sheet iron and the other of either sheet copper or brass. The ends of these metal strips should be pressed together as tightly as possible. If the young builder can handle a soldering iron, he can solder the ends together.

click will be heard in the headphone, proving that electricity is being generated.

The young experimenter, however, should not be led to think that a thermoelectric cell such as this will generate any great amount of electricity. Only a very small amount will be produced—not even enough to operate the smallest toy electric motor.

If the experimenter wishes, the candle shown to supply heat to the cell may be replaced by a small alcohol burner.

Chapter 14

THE SOLAR BATTERY

A NEW way of converting (changing) the heat of
the sun directly into electric current has been found.
This is done with a special form of electric generator
now called a silicon solar battery. Such batteries
have now become so reliable that they are being
used in industry.

Silicon solar cells can be purchased from most
electronic or radio supply houses* and are relatively
inexpensive. They are provided with terminals like
ordinary dry cells. Small nuts are used to hold the
wires to the cells when they are in use. The terminals

*Lafayette Radio and Electronics, 165–08 Liberty Ave., Jamaica 33,
N.Y., for one.

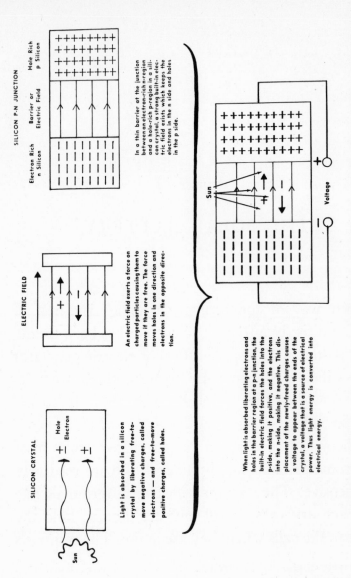

Fig. 31. How the Bell solar battery works. Soon much of the world's power supply may be generated with such batteries. (Courtesy Bell Telephone Laboratories)

of each cell are marked + and − (or positive and negative) as in the case of ordinary cells, either wet or dry. Silicon solar or heat cells are also connected the same way as other types. (See Figure 1, page 22.)

However, silicon solar cells are not so powerful as ordinary cells, that is, not in the form in which they may now be purchased. As many as four of them properly connected have combined power enough to turn only a tiny, especially made electric motor. Indeed, a battery made up of four cells of this type will only generate about .9 volt and 40–50 milliamperes (a milliampere equals one-thousandth of an ampere). A single dry cell of the sort that is used today will deliver 1 ½ volts with a maximum of about 20 full amperes.

Nevertheless, the silicon solar cell is a most interesting generator and it is not known how much it will be improved over the coming years.

As might be suspected, solar cells generate most current at high noon during the summertime, when the sun is hottest, on a clear day. But they may also be used on dark days without the sun. The young experimenter need only place a powerful electric

Fig. 32. Talking with solar-electric power. The man in the foreground is holding a silicon strip solar battery. The sun's rays striking this battery generate an electric current. This current is used to power a telephone circuit over which the man in the foreground is talking to the man in the background. (Courtesy Bell Telephone Laboratories)

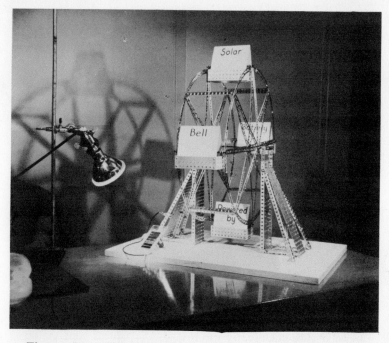

Fig. 33. A toy Ferris wheel is turned by a toy electric motor receiving its power from the solar battery shown beneath the powerful electric light. It is the energy from this light that is converted into electricity and used to turn the motor.
(Courtesy Bell Telephone Laboratories)

light or heat lamp in front of the solar cell or battery and it will immediately begin to generate electric current.

While the solar cell operates with heat, it should not be confused with the thermoelectric cell dis-

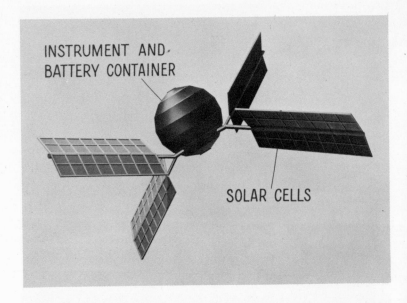

Fig. 34. Drawing of the paddle-wheel satellite. A large number of solar cells enclosed in the thin paddle wheels convert the energy of the sun into electricity. The solar cells then recharge the chemical batteries inside the sphere. The solar cell may prove to be the answer to one of the most difficult problems of space vehicles — that of a continuing source of power to operate the vehicle's instruments and radio transmitters. The first paddle-wheel satellite was launched in August of 1959. (Courtesy National Aeronautics and Space Administration)

cussed in Chapter 13. Though the thermoelectric cell might generate a small electric current if the rays from the sun were focused on it, the principle involved is not quite the same. The silicon solar battery would be far more efficient.

Some of us may well live to see the day when solar batteries will be so large that they will cover many acres of ground and supply our country with much of its electricity for use in home and industry. There are already sun-powered portable radios on the market.

Each day of our lives the sun sheds some 125 trillion horsepower of energy on the earth. This is far more than we need. It is indeed a pity that we cannot learn to capture some of this energy for our everyday needs. Newer and more efficient forms of the silicon battery may be able to do this sooner than most of us think. It could even be that solar energy, there for the taking, will make the use of atomic energy unnecessary. The so-called Atomic Age may well give way to the safer Solar Age.

Chapter 15

THE ATOMIC BATTERY

ELECTRIC current may be generated in many different ways. The latest method of producing current is that of converting atomic energy directly into electric current. This is done through a small new cell which is called an atomic cell by the company that produced it, the Radio Corporation of America.

The young experimenter cannot hope to make his own atomic cell or battery at this time. He cannot purchase one either. The author is including this chapter on the atomic battery merely to give the young reader some idea of the exciting advances that are being made in the field of science and electronics.

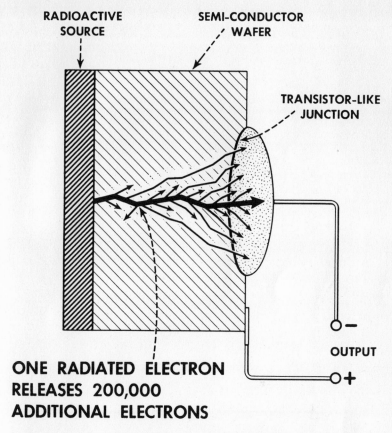

RADIOACTIVE
SOURCE

SEMI-CONDUCTOR
WAFER

TRANSISTOR-LIKE
JUNCTION

OUTPUT

**ONE RADIATED ELECTRON
RELEASES 200,000
ADDITIONAL ELECTRONS**

Fig. 35. How an atomic cell is constructed. The shaded section at the extreme left is made up of strontium 90, a product of the fission of uranium in an atomic reactor. The more lightly shaded portion of the cell is made of a semi-conductor (half-efficient conductor) such as the element silicon. A single electron released from the strontium serves as a trigger to release 200,000 electrons that flow to the terminals of the cell and thereby form a small electric current. (Courtesy Radio Corporation of America)

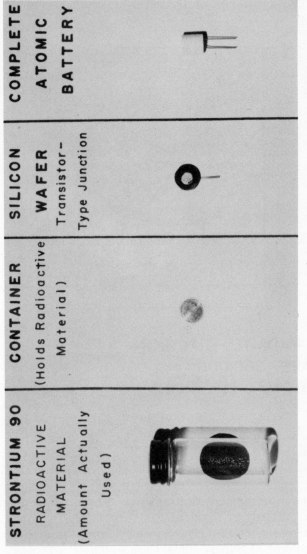

| STRONTIUM 90 | CONTAINER | SILICON | COMPLETE |
| RADIOACTIVE MATERIAL (Amount Actually Used) | (Holds Radioactive Material) | WAFER Transistor-Type Junction | ATOMIC BATTERY |

Fig. 36. The materials and parts that enter into the construction of the atomic cell. The completed cell is very small, about the size of a thimble. It produces very little electric current. (Courtesy Radio Corporation of America)

Most young men of this day know that electric current is made up of tiny particles bouncing along at high speed through wires and electrical machinery and instruments of all kinds. These tiny particles that have never been seen are called electrons. Although never seen, instruments have detected and measured them.

Every time an electric light is turned on or one speaks over the telephone, billions upon billions of these tiny electrons rush through the wires connected to the light or the telephone.

Although to date the atomic cell is able to deliver only a small fraction of a volt and a still smaller fraction of an ampere, the device does break the ground of a major new field of scientific research.

Soon there may be larger atomic batteries, perhaps batteries large enough to run automobiles or heat homes. Certainly there will be atomic batteries powerful enough to operate radios and other small power-consuming devices. In the future there will no doubt be atomic batteries that will release many billions of electrons every second.

Unlike the ordinary batteries that we have in use today, such as storage batteries and dry or wet bat-

Fig. 37. A magnified view of an atomic cell in its final stages of assembly. Here the transistor-like junction is being put in place. The position of this junction is shown in Fig. 35. (Courtesy Radio Corporation of America)

teries, the atomic batteries will last for many years
without being recharged in any manner. Indeed, such
batteries will be lifetime batteries. They will go on
and on without interruption and without failure.

Whereas today the power of an atomic battery
could be measured in terms of flypower only, the
atomic battery of the future will no doubt be measured in terms of horsepower.